nsed exclusi

...is...

Tide Mill Media

...ghts reserved

... 4 6 8 ... 7 5 3 1

Manufactured in China

Written by Susie Linn

Illustrated by Natalia Moore

ISBN 978-1-78700-5587

"For Sarah, always an angel." SL

What an Angel!

Written by Susie Linn

Illustrated by Natalia Moore

Mom and Grandma gazed down at the new baby.

"Isn't she sweet?
Isn't she adorable?"
sighed Mom.

"What an angel!" whispered Grandma.

"That's it!" said Mom.
"That's what I'm going to call her...Angel!"

But Mom and Grandma were in for a surprise.

On the day of the Beautiful Baby Contest, "sweet," "adorable" Angel was tired of waiting for her turn.

BLIP...BLOP...BLOOP...
went the lovely, oozy mud,
as Angel made her first mud pie ever.

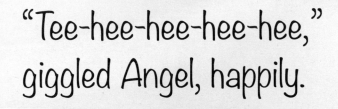

"Tee-hee-hee-hee-hee," giggled Angel, happily.

At Angel's friend Daisy's fifth birthday party,
all the little girls were busy decorating cupcakes with
frosting and delicate sugar candies. All except for Angel.

"...Seven, eight, nine..." counted Angel,
as she built her very own candy-treat tower,
joining the cupcakes together with lots of gooey frosting.

"Ten!" squealed Angel, as her tower teetered...wobbled...and then fell over!

One Saturday, Grandma took Angel to the mall
to buy some pretty pink ballet slippers.

But Angel had a different plan.

"Wow!" cried Angel, stomping around the store in a pair of big, shiny red boots.

At school, Angel loved science most of all.

While the other children worked quietly,
doing their great science experiments,
Angel was busy with an experiment of her own.

WHIZZZZ... BANG...

FIZZZZZ...

KERPOW!

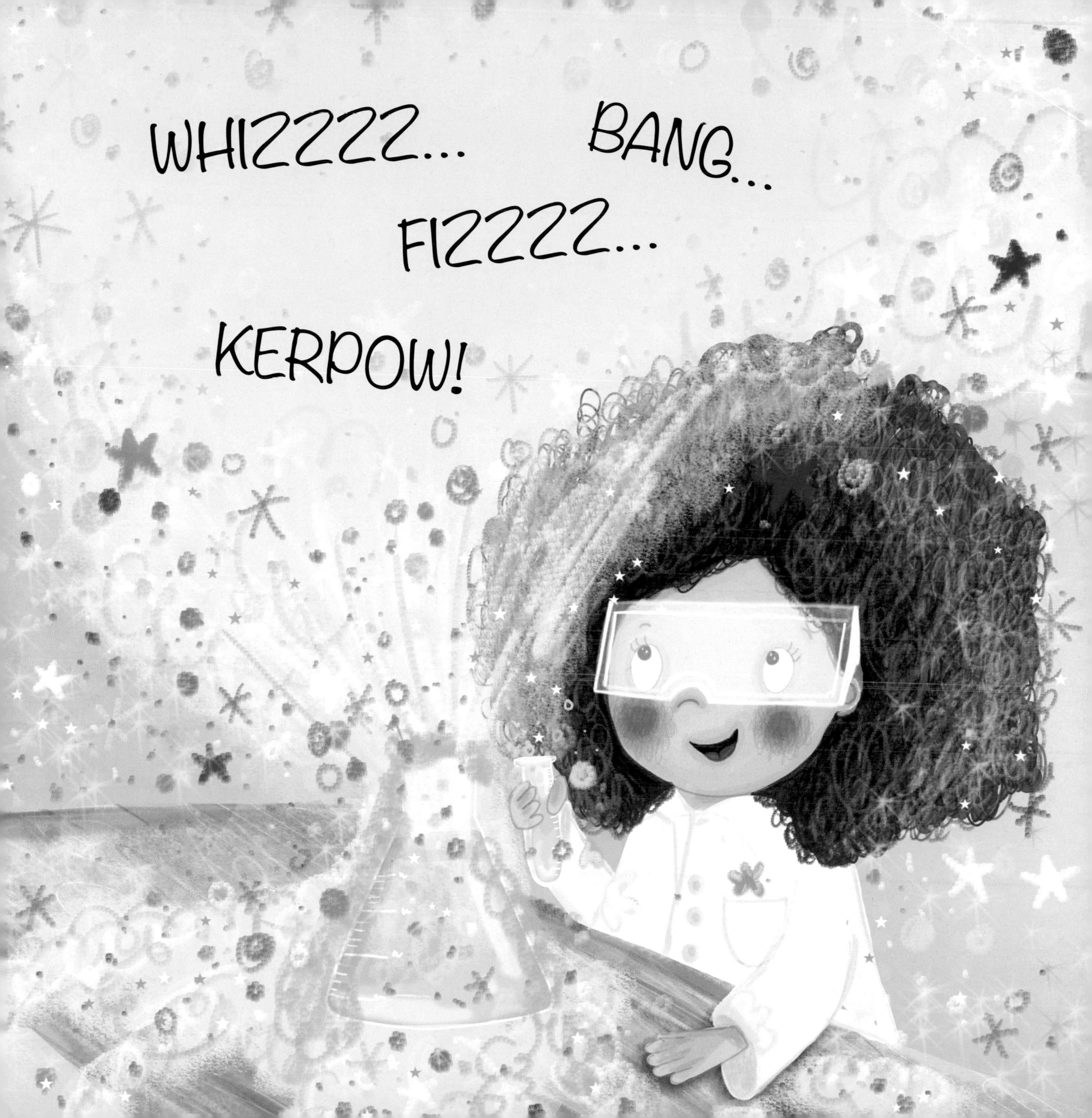

"Angel...how about learning to play a musical instrument?" suggested Mom one day. "Like the recorder, or maybe the flute?" she said, hopefully.

One week later...KERRRANG!
KERCHANG! KERTWANG!
went Angel's electric guitar,
as she ran her hand
over the strings.

Everyone wanted Angel to change,
but Angel was very happy just
being herself.

It was almost the end of the year when Angel spotted a poster on the school noticeboard.

FAME-FACTOR
TALENT CONTEST
Saturday December 20th
In the School Hall
APPLY NOW!

The evening of the Fame-factor Talent Contest arrived.
Group after group of children took to the stage.

They played
piano duets...

acted out scenes from plays...

sang...

played the recorder...

read poems...

and told jokes.

Then, at long last,
it was Angel's turn.

The lights went down and the curtain went up.

There was a loud KERRRANG!...and Angel,
in her red boots and denim, with her wild, wild hair,
took to the stage with her electric guitar.

And she was AMAZING!

"Angel! Angel! Angel!"
the audience yelled in excitement.

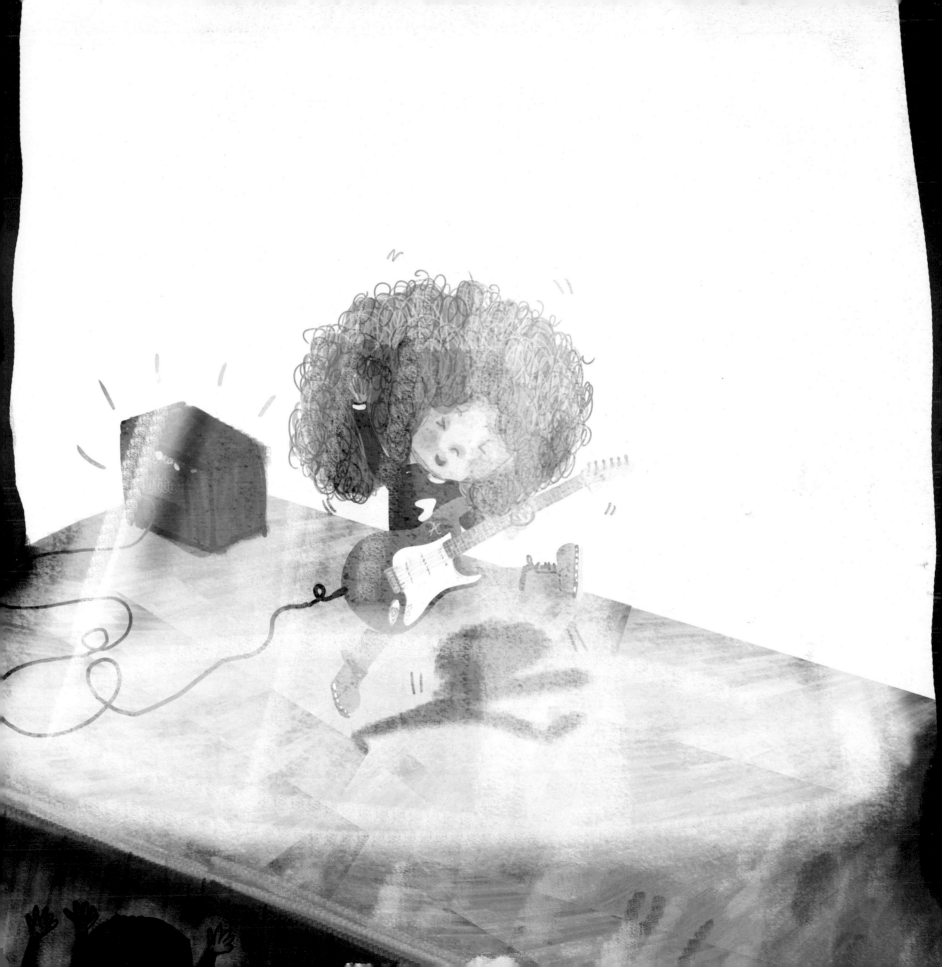

The guest judge was as impressed as the audience.

"And the first prize goes to...ANGEL!"

"YES!" cried Angel, jumping up and down.

Being herself was just GREAT!

And it was just the beginning...